IF YOU GIVE A MOOSE A MUFFIN

by Laura Joffe Numeroff

illustrated by Felicia Bond

SCHOLASTIC INC.

New York Toronto London Auckland Sydney

ISBN 0-590-45508-7

Text Copyright © 1991 by Laura Numeroff.
Illustrations copyright © 1991 by Felicia Bond.
All rights reserved. Published by Scholastic Inc.,
730 Broadway, New York, NY 10003,
by arrangement with HarperCollins Publishers.

35 34   9/9 0 1/0

Printed in the U.S.A.   09

First Scholastic printing, September 1992